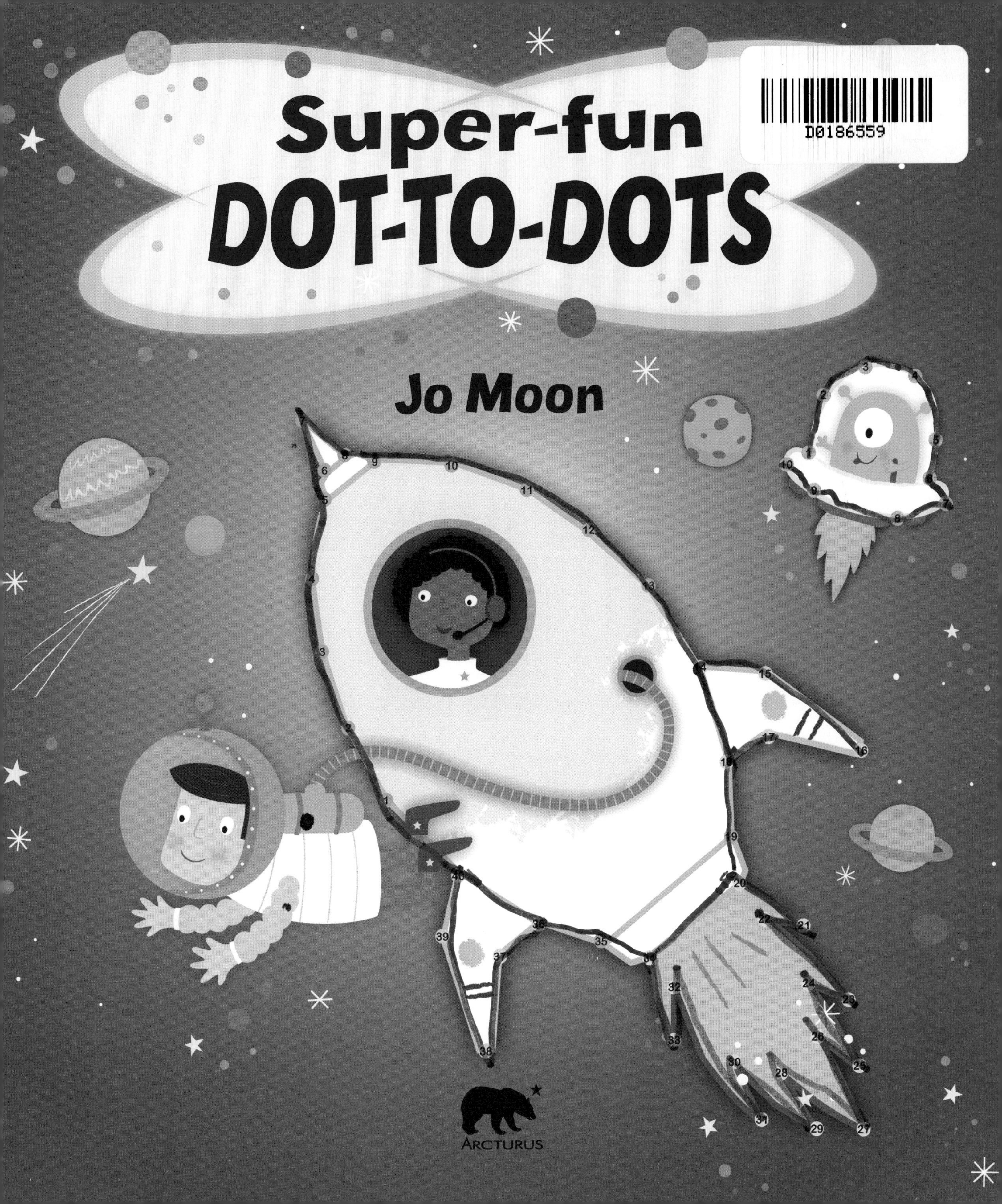
Super-fun
DOT-TO-DOTS
Jo Moon
ARCTURUS

This edition published in 2016 by Arcturus Publishing Limited
26/27 Bickels Yard, 151–153 Bermondsey Street,
London SE1 3HA

Illustrations: Jo Moon
Text: JMS Books llp
Design by Chris Bell
Editor: Joe Harris

ISBN: 978-1-78599-228-5
CH004906NT
Supplier: 26, Date 0916, Print run 5721

Printed in China

Aladdin's Lamp

Something inside the magic lamp has escaped. Connect the dots to see what it is.

Dinosaur Roar!

Join the dots to reveal two prehistoric creatures about to have a battle!

Many scientists think that the two-legged dinosaurs had feathers.

They couldn't fly, but feathers would keep them warm.

Jungle Fun

Imagine that you're exploring a jungle. Which animals will you discover?

Tigers are the biggest and strongest members of the cat family.
Some monkeys can use their tails to hang from tree branches.

To the Rescue

Join the dots to find out who is going to save this big city from attack by aliens.

The Empire State Building has 103 floors and 6,514 windows.
The tallest buildings are called "skyscrapers."

Pet Store

The two pets hidden in this picture both like to eat carrots and lettuce. What are they?

Rabbits usually live for about 10 years.
Tortoises sometimes live for 100 years!

Pop Stars

Find out what the members of this band are doing on stage at their concert.

Electric guitars usually have six strings but can have up to twelve.
The loudness of a sound is measured in "decibels."

Fun Fair

See what exciting rides these children can enjoy at the fun fair today.

1 2 3 4 5 6 7 8 9 10 11 12 13 14 15 16 17 18 19 20 21 22 23 24 25 26 27 28 29 30 31 32 33 34 35 36 37 38 39 40 41 42 43 44 45 46 47 48 49 50 51 52 53 54 55 56 57

Some roller coaster rides are as tall as skyscrapers.

The big wheel carrying people in a circle is called a "Ferris wheel."

Under the Sea

*Join the dots to see below the sea.
Which creatures are swimming about?*

Sharks can be as small as your hand or as big as a bus.

There are around 300 species of octopus. They have eight arms and blue blood!

1 2 3 4 5 6 7 8 9 10 11 12 13 14 15 16 17 18 19 20 21 22 23 24 25 26 27 28 29 30 31 32 33 34 35 36 37 38 39 40 41 42 43 44 45 46 47 48 49 50 51 52 53 54 55 56 57 58 59 60 61 62 63 64 65 66 67 68 69 70 71 72 73 74 75 76 77 78 79 80

Traffic Jam

"Are we there yet?" Discover the different types of vehicle that are stuck in this jam by connecting all the dots.

There are more than one billion cars in the world.
The very first cars were powered by steam!

Dragon Quest

A scary creature is trying to reach the big building on the hill. Can the brave knights chase it away?

Mountain Climb

Some people and animals are good at climbing steep slopes. Find out who is on the way up the mountain today.

The hooves of mountain goats are the perfect shape for climbing.
Young goats are called kids. Just like you!

On the Beach

Join the dots to find two things beginning with "c" on the sandy beach on this warm, sunny day.

Sand can be white, gold, brown, red, or black.
Crabs have eyes on stalks, just like snails.

Lily Pond Pals

Three water-loving creatures are enjoying the pond in this picture. Find out which ones they are!

Frogs use their long, sticky tongues to catch flies.
A special oil makes ducks' feathers waterproof.

Knights' Combat

These two knights are about to have a duel. Which one do you think will win?

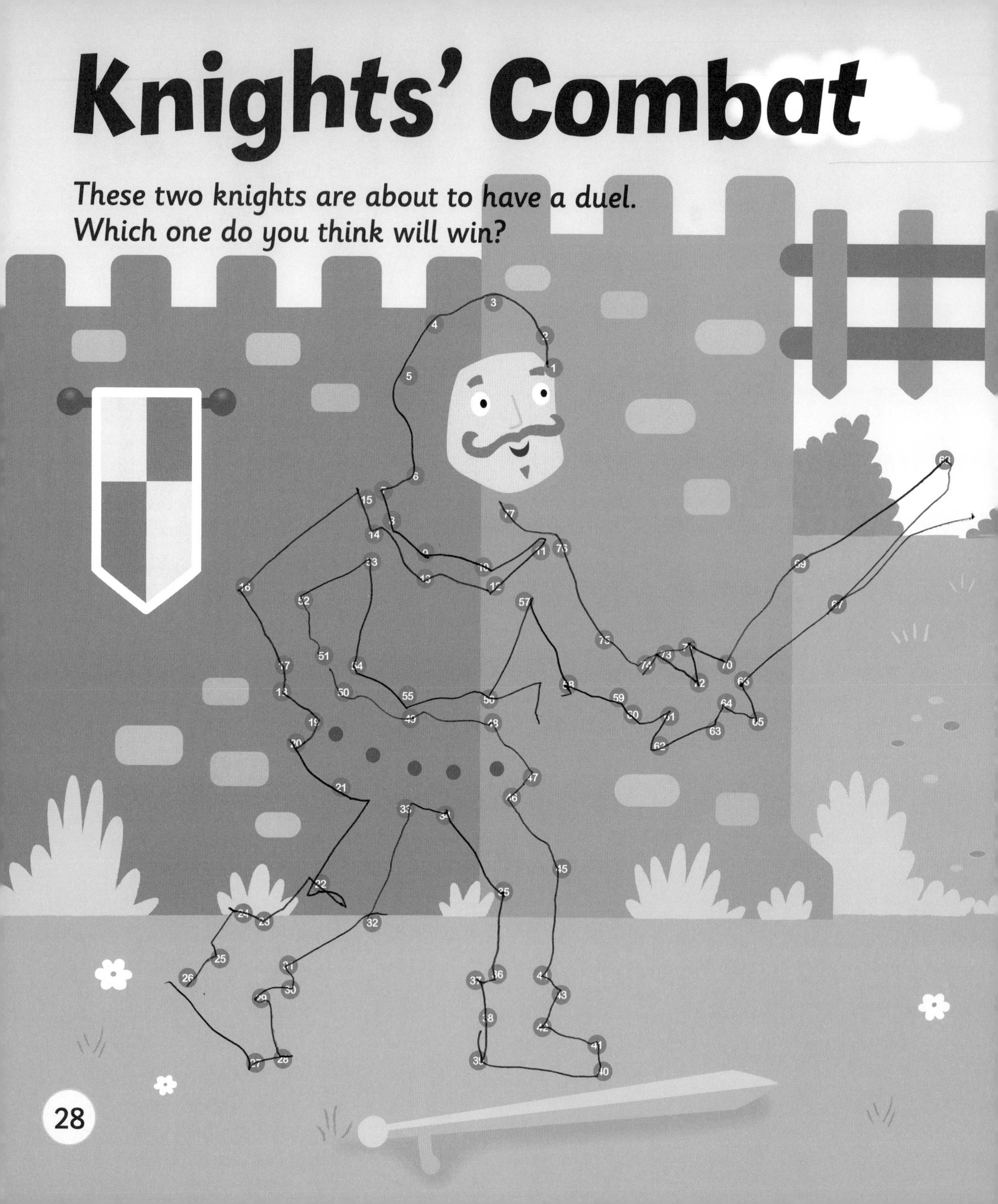

Knights rode around on horseback.
They had assistants called "squires" who carried their shields.

Ancient Mysteries

Which country do you think is shown in this picture?
Do you know what the strange creature is called?

Pyramids were built for kings to be buried in.
They are more than three thousand years old.

Let's Build!

These two builders are working hard to make new roads and houses. Do you know what their vehicles are called?

Diggers have big buckets to pick up their loads.
The buckets are made of very strong metal.

Let's Go Camping!

Join the yellow and blue dots to see two things that will keep you warm when you camp out at night.

Only adults should start campfires.

Tents are made of thin fabric and protect people from the wind and rain.

Branch Buddies

These two creatures spend lots of time on branches in the tropical forests. What are they?

There are more than 350 types of parrot in the world.
Most snakes and parrots prefer to live in warm places.

Happy Birthday!

Join the pink and blue dots to see what these kids are doing at their birthday party.

The first teddy bear was made over one hundred years ago.
It was named after an American president called Teddy Roosevelt.

On the Farm

Which happy animal is frolicking in this field? Who is his friend?

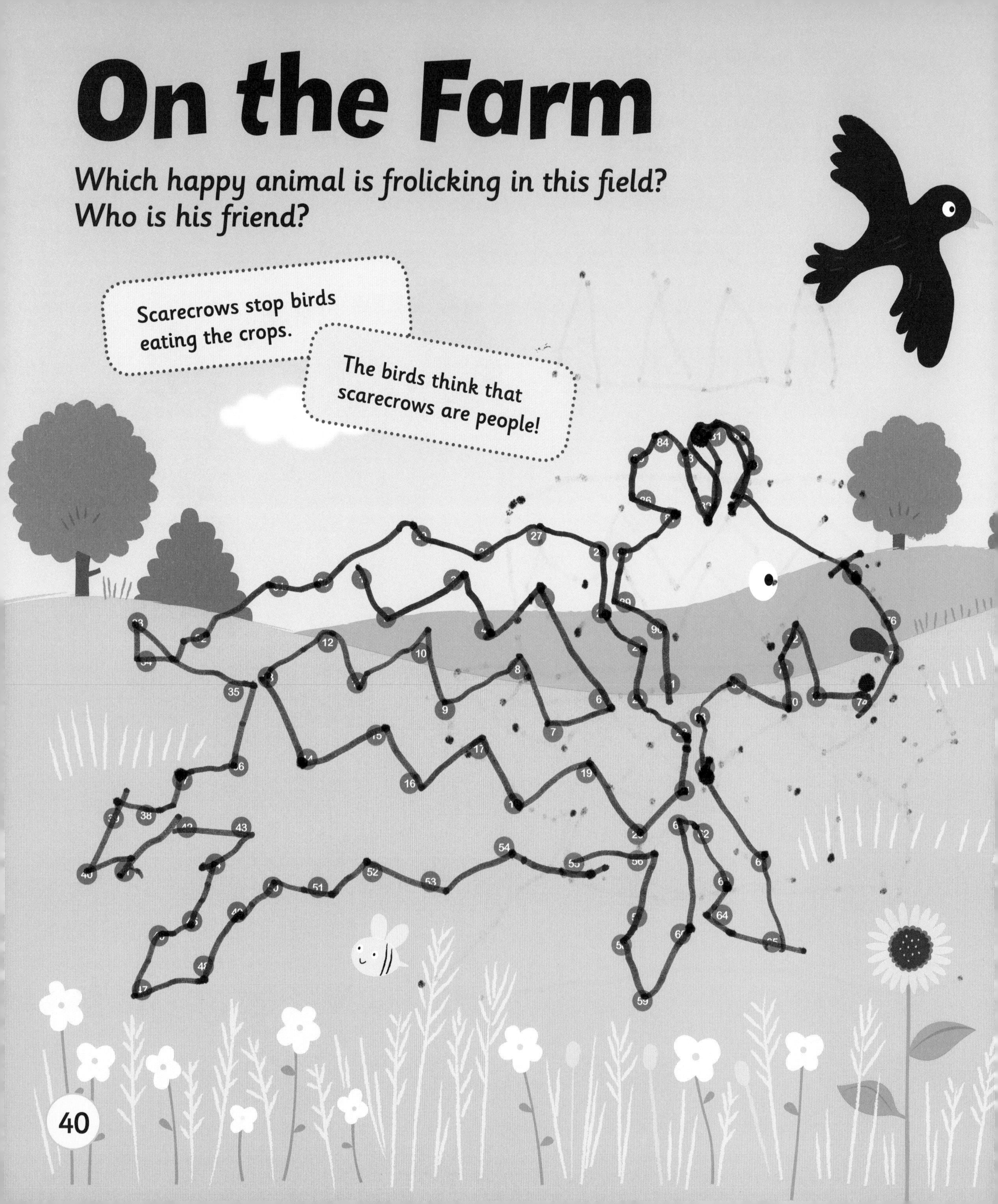

Busy Bugs

Join the three sets of dots to see what is happening in this flower garden in the summer.

Fit for a King

Who is enjoying this wonderful feast? Who else is at the table?

In medieval times the job of court jesters was to amuse the king.
The jester would wear a floppy hat with jingle bells.

Outer Space

Find out who is exploring this alien planet... and who he is about to meet!

Nobody knows for sure if aliens exist or not.
Some people call them "E.T.," which means extra terrestial.

Windy Day

Join the red, orange, and blue dots to see what is flying high in the sky on this blustery day.

Eagles have very good eyesight.
They build their nests in tall trees.
8
14
18
20
11
7
21
19
6
9
10
12
13
15
17
4
5
16
1
3
2

Ride the Ferry

Welcome to New York City! Join the dots to reveal a ferry boat and a very famous statue.

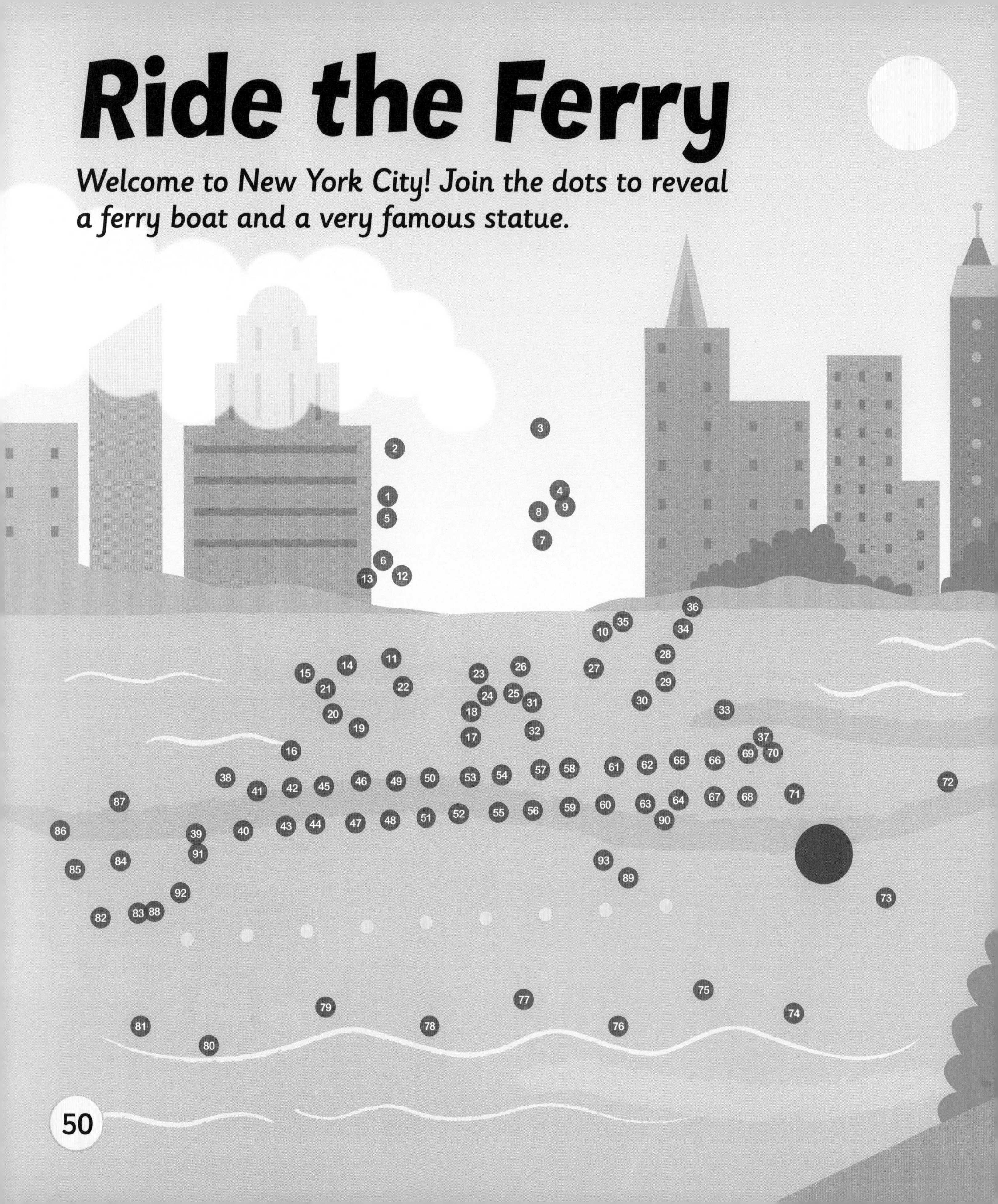

The Statue of Liberty was given to America by France.
It was a gift of friendship between the two countries.

Water Hole

Which large animals have come to drink the water in the African heat?

Home Run!

Join the red and blue dots to see what exciting game these two are playing.

30
6
35
The batter hits the ball as far as he can.
If he can run around all four bases, he scores a run.

Desert Dreams

What kind of animals live in this hot, dry desert? Join the dots to find out.

Meerkats stand on their hind legs and keep watch.
Camels can have two humps or just one.

Music Maestro

Which instrument is the musician playing?
And what is the other person doing?

A conductor stands in front of the orchestra.
He or she makes sure that everybody joins in at the right time.

Flower Bed

Find out which insect is buzzing around the pretty flowers in this garden.

46 47 48 51 50 45 52 43 42 49 44 30 29 53 41 31 19 18 17 28 54 55 40 9 10 56 39 32 20 3 2 8 16 27 38 11 4 1 37 33 21 7 57 12 5 6 15 22 26 59 58 34 13 14 36 84 35 23 85 25 60 69 88 24 64 86 61 68 63 83 87 65 62 67 82 81 70 66 73 72 71 74 80 77 75 76 79 78

Bees collect nectar from flowers.

They use the nectar to make delicious honey.

Circus Fun

The circus has come to town. Which performers can you find in the ring?

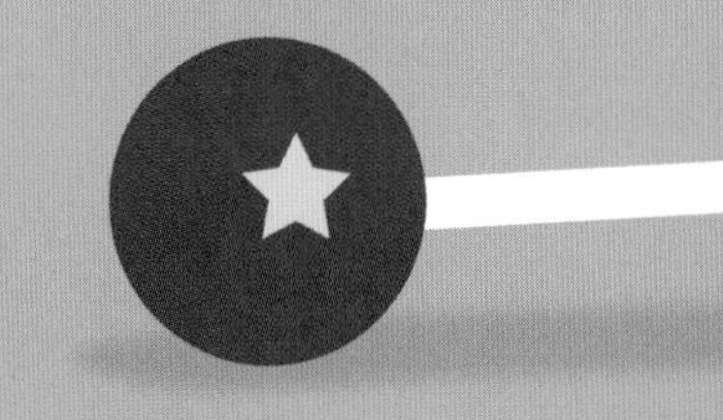

Clowns wear silly clothes and big red noses.
It is their job to make you smile.

Kitchen Capers

Find out who makes all the mess in this busy kitchen... and who cleans it up!

Chefs usually wear white coats.
Their tall hats are called "toques."

Down on the Farm

Join the dots to see which vehicle the farmer is driving and who is watching him.

A tractor usually has just one seat.
The tractor can pull along a trailer.

On the Ranch

What kind of animal is running around on this ranch? And just what is the cowboy up to?

Cattle ranches are large farms for raising cattle.
The rope used to catch cattle is called a "lasso."

Polar Pals

These playful animals don't mind the cold. Join the dots to find another animal... and a warm place to stay!

Polar bears are fast swimmers with great underwater vision.
Penguins can also swim but they cannot fly.

A Day in the Park

What a lovely day for a stroll in the park! Join the dots to reveal two people and an animal.

Skateboarding was invented by surfers in California.
They wanted to be able to surf even without waves!

Spells Galore

Abracadabra! Join the dots to see who is casting a magic spell.

In stories, witches ride on broomsticks.
They often have a pet cat to help them with their spells.

What Goes Up...

Find out who is coming to the rescue of the poor kitty stuck in the tree.

Firefighters often have to climb very high.

They save people from burning buildings and scared cats from trees.

Sports Arena

These two athletes are competing at different sports. Find out which ones.

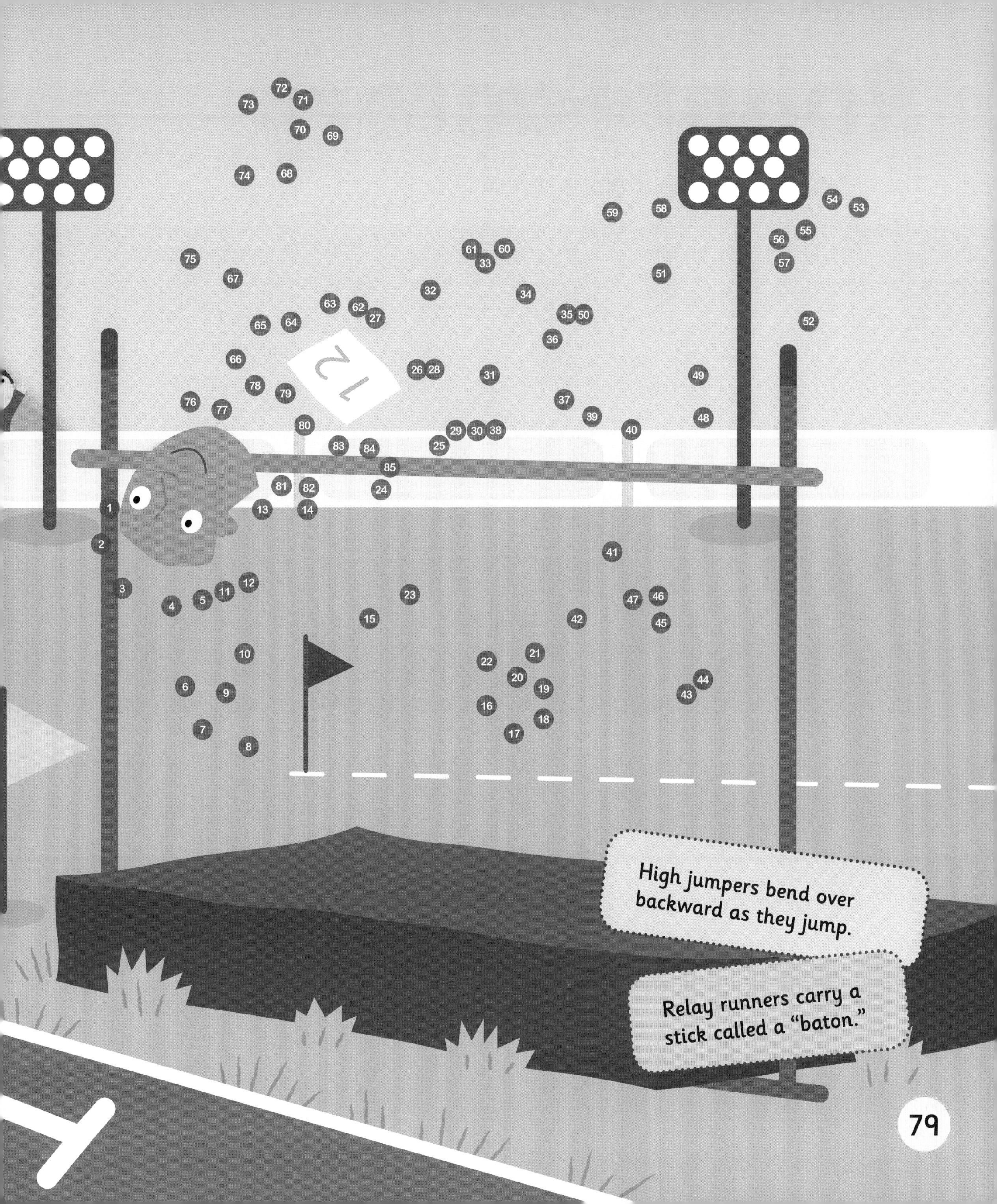
High jumpers bend over backward as they jump.
Relay runners carry a stick called a "baton."

Robot Factory

Join the red and blue dots to meet two mechanical friends.

Riding the Surf

It's a windy day at sea! Join the dots to see who is playing in the waves.

Dolphins love to jump out of the water and ride the waves.
Sometimes they play with humans in the water, too.

Haunted House

There is something spooky going on in this old house. Find out what it is.

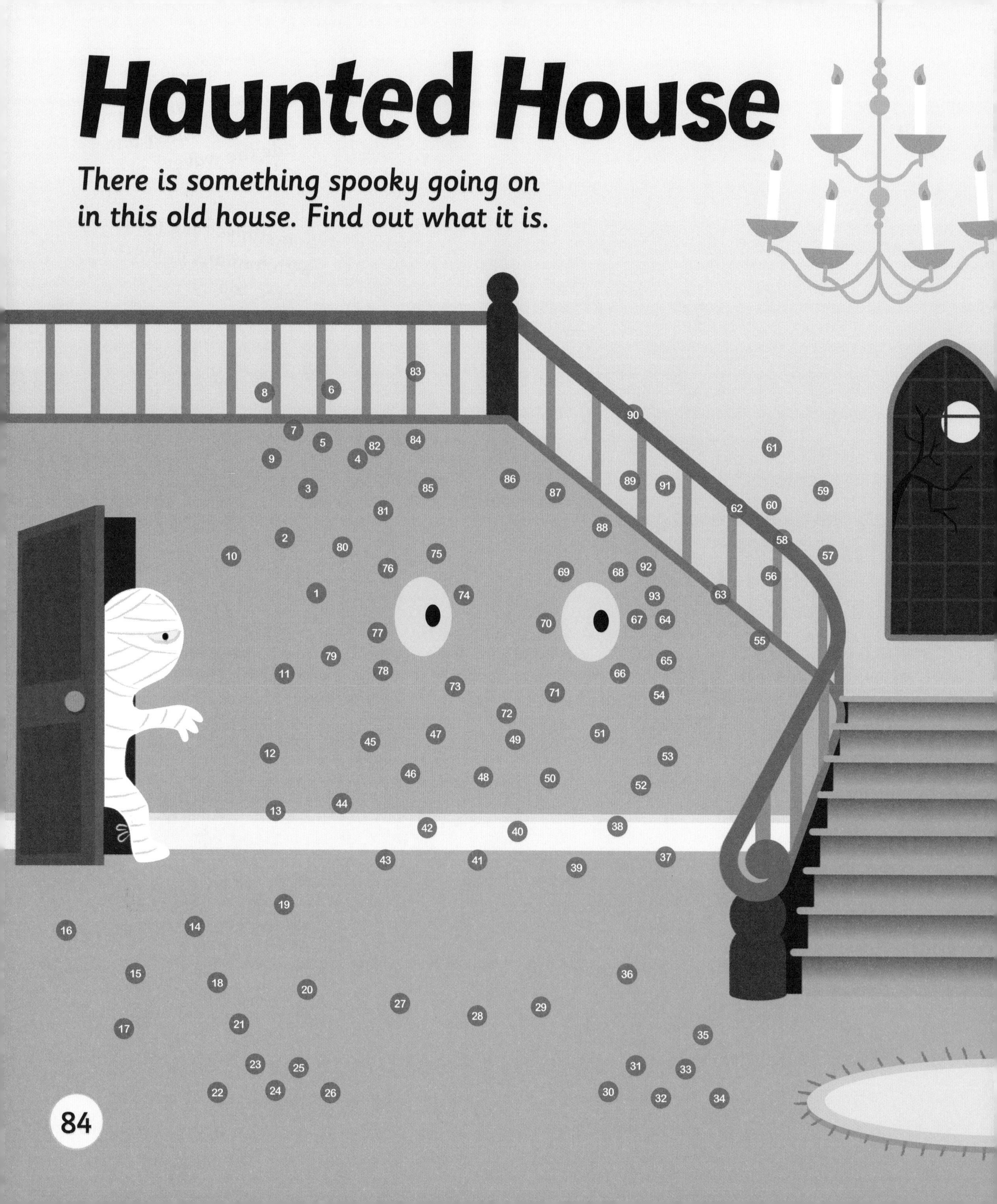

Every year on Halloween night...
...ghosts and ghouls will give you a fright!

Treasure Island

Somewhere in this picture is a box full of gold and treasure. Join all the dots to find it!

Up, Up, and Away!

Everyone is taking to the skies on this beautiful day. Which machines are they flying in?

The first hot-air balloon flight was more than 200 years ago.
The hot air in the balloon makes it lift up into the sky!

Solutions

On the following pages we show you what was hidden in the pictures. Once you have joined the dots, your drawings should look just like these.

Pages 10–11
Pages 12–13
Pages 14–15
Pages 16–17
Pages 18–19
Pages 20–21
Pages 22–23
Pages 24–25

Pages 26–27

Pages 28–29

Pages 30–31

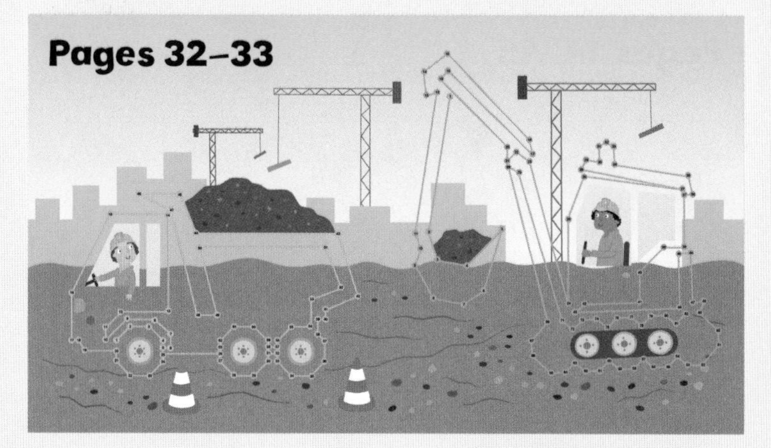
Pages 32–33

Pages 34–35

Pages 36–37

Pages 38–39

Pages 40–41

Pages 42–43
Pages 46–47

Pages 44–45

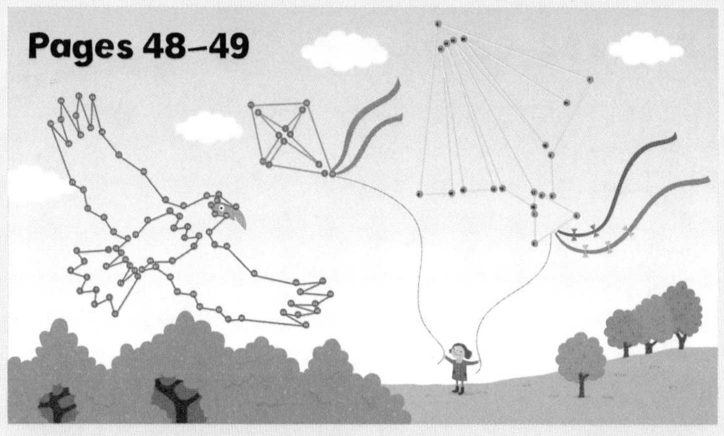
Pages 48–49

Pages 50–51

Pages 52–53

Pages 54–55
30 6 35

Pages 56–57

Pages 58–59

Pages 60–61

Pages 62–63

Pages 64–65

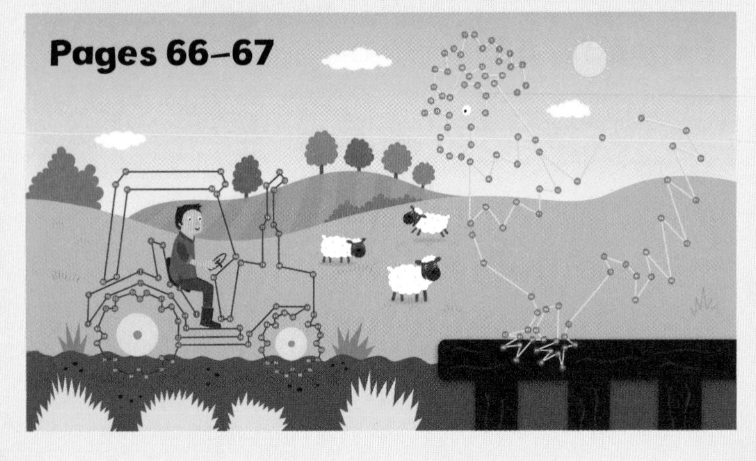
Pages 66–67

Pages 68–69

Pages 70–71

Pages 72–73

Pages 74–75

Pages 76–77

Pages 78–79
15

Pages 80–81

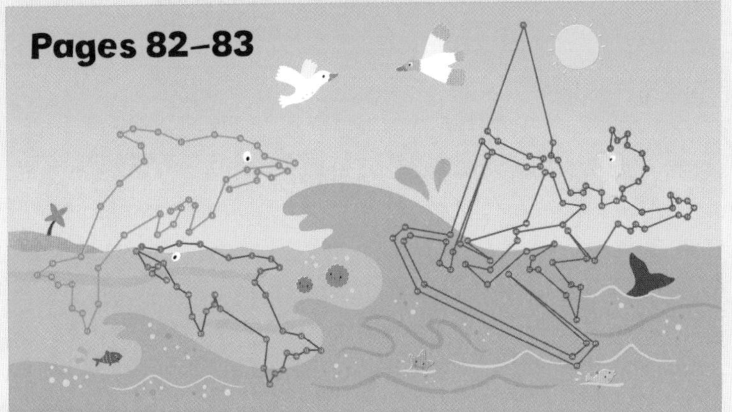
Pages 82–83

Pages 84–85

Pages 86–87

Pages 88–89

We hope you enjoyed this "dotty" book!